P9-BYD-048

THE
SEMINOLE INDIANS

The
SEMINOLE
INDIANS

By SONIA BLEEKER

Illustrated by Althea Karr

WILLIAM MORROW & COMPANY
New York · 1954

Seventh Printing, December, 1966

2/25

Grateful recognition is given to
Professor John N. Goggin,
Department of Sociology and Anthropology,
University of Florida, Gainesville, Florida,
for reading and criticizing the manuscript.

CONTENTS

THE
SEMINOLE INDIANS

1

TO THE SWAMPS

THE boy was trotting behind his mother. He tried to stretch his short brown legs so he would step right into her footprints. If he stepped into them quickly, just as she lifted her foot, the footprint was still dry. If he fell just one step behind, the water seeped into her footprint and it felt cold

and slippery underfoot. His embroidered buckskin moccasins had become soggy on the swampy
trail. At first the boy had not dared take them off.
His mother had said, "Keep your moccasins on,
Little Owl. The grass will cut your feet." She
meant the three-edged, spiny saw grass which
grew in the wet spots along the trail. But the moccasins were so wet and heavy that the boy finally
slipped them off. He wrung the water out of them
and tucked them into his belt.

In the first days of their march into Florida
from their homeland—now southern Georgia and
Alabama—all the people had worn moccasins.
Mother had brought along several pairs for herself and for her son in her burden basket. She
carried the burden basket on her back, strapped
across her chest with a braided buckskin rope. But
most of the moccasins had worn out long ago. Pair
after pair had been thrown away along the trail.
Now Mother, like the rest of the people on the
march, was barefooted.

Their clothing was beginning to wear out too, although the well-tanned buckskin leggings which the men wore and the women's short, knee-length skirts and capes were still in good condition. The fringes on Little Owl's leggings were ragged, but the buckskin of the leggings themselves was still good. In the hot Florida sun, however, they felt heavy and clung to the boy's sweating legs. He would have liked to take them off but was afraid he would fall too far behind.

Last night his mother had rubbed him, as well as herself, with fish oil so the mosquitoes and other insects would not bother him. The mosquitoes did not actually sting him now, but they swarmed about and he kept fanning them away with both hands. This made the boy even more tired, and he fell out of step.

He had been walking ever since dawn, when he had eaten a hurried breakfast. The sun was hot and his throat was parched. He tugged at his mother's burden basket and she turned and smiled

down at him, encouraging him to go on.

"Come, son," she said. "You are a good runner. Your legs are so much longer now."

The praise pleased Little Owl. Again he fell into step, his toes sinking into Mother's dry footprints. But after a few steps he fell behind once more. Mother took his hand and together they stepped off the trail, out of the way of the file of people behind them.

The tired, sweaty, grim faces were familiar to the boy. The tall, lean men with their fringed buckskins, their necklaces, earrings, and arm bands, walked with steady, long strides. Many carried heavy guns; some had bows and arrows and spears. Most of them had long metal knives tucked into their wide buckskin belts. The women who marched behind the men were short and heavy-set. They were loaded down with burden baskets, and many were carrying babies on their backs or small children too young to march.

This entire Indian village was moving to Florida. They were Creek Indians whom the white settlers had forced out of their lands farther north. The year was 1808, when Florida still belonged to Spain, and the Spanish government welcomed Indian settlers.

Early Spanish explorers and conquerors had found Florida peopled with about fifty Indian tribes. There may have been as many as twenty thousand people in Florida when Ponce de Leon first landed on its eastern coast on April 2, 1513. He was searching for the Fountain of Youth as well as for riches, and he named the peninsula in honor of the Easter Festival, *La Florida*. At that time the most numerous Indians on the east coast of Florida were the Timucuan, who were mainly farmers and fishermen. At first they were quite friendly to the Spaniards.

Hernando de Soto landed on the shores of

Tampa Bay, on the west coast of Florida, in 1539. His aim was to explore and conquer Florida and the land beyond for the Spanish Crown. The powerful and numerous Calusa tribes, who lived on the west coast, were unfriendly; the Spanish called them "the fierce people." The Calusa fought the Spanish, the French, the English, and finally the troops of the United States, till almost all of these Indians perished.

In the northwest part of the peninsula lived the Apalachee. De Soto spent the winter of 1539 with them. The Apalachee were farmers and great warriors, too. They fought the Spanish at first, but later they invited Spanish missionaries to their towns and for a time enjoyed great prosperity. Then the Creek Indians who lived to the north, in Alabama and Georgia, fought the Apalachee, with the help of the English. In 1704 an army of white men, under Governor Moore of Carolina, and a thousand Indian allies attacked the Apalachee and took about fifteen hundred of them back to Carolina as slaves. A year later another expedition of white troops and Indians wiped out almost the entire Apalachee population.

So by 1750, when the Creek migrations to Florida began, the Indian tribes who had lived in Florida for hundreds of years—the Timucuan, Calusa, and Apalachee—had almost disappeared. All but a few survivors had been destroyed by wars and by diseases brought in by the white men —measles, smallpox, diphtheria. Some of the survivors retreated south to the swamps and to the Keys; others migrated to Cuba.

When the Creek tribes were forced out of their own territory, they found ample land in central Florida, and it was here that this Creek boy, Little Owl, and his people planned to make their new home. They had heard from other Indians and from escaping Negro slaves, who frequently stopped off at their village for a night's rest, that it was even warmer in Florida than in their homeland. "Plenty of land and water there," the escaping slaves had said. "White men don't like the Florida swamps, and the Spanish government lets us live in peace."

Little Owl's uncle had done everything he could to help the mother and her son since the father's death two years before. After talking with the escaped slaves, Little Owl's uncle had decided to go to Florida with the rest of the village. He had said to the boy's mother, "Come with us, Sister. We will all stay together. Little Owl can grow up in freedom—in the ways of the Indian, not of the white man."

The families began packing soon after the Green Corn Dance, the yearly dance of thanksgiving to the Creator, which all the Creek celebrated. That year the Green Corn Dance, the boy recalled, was not a happy festival like the one held the year before. They were all sad about leaving the land where they, their fathers, and their forefathers had always lived. The crops had been good, and they thanked the Creator for his kindness. But their sadness was greater because of the good crops and because of the cleared fields they had to leave behind them. They had labored hard and now this fertile farm land would be lost to them.

By the time the corn had been harvested and hulled and the beans and melons dried and packed into burden baskets, the weather had turned colder and the people were ready to leave for Florida. The village chief, or *miko*, and the men, with their guns, knives, and bows and arrows, marched at the front. The women, children, and pack horses followed behind.

It was for one of these horses that Little Owl and his mother were now waiting. When one of them came up close, with a child already sitting on top of the bundles of food and household goods, Mother lifted the boy up on the horse, too, and took her place again in the line of marchers.

Little Owl pulled off his leggings, leaned

against a basket full of beans, and wiped some of the oil and sweat off his body with his hands. He felt more cool and comfortable with nothing on but his breechcloth.

Looking about from the new height, he could see much more of the country than he had seen while trudging behind his mother. He thought Florida far more beautiful than his homeland. Around him stretched a grassy rolling plain with scattered clumps of pines, oaks, and palmettos. Everywhere Spanish moss covered clumps of pine and oak. The moss gave the treetops an untidy, ragged look. The boy thought the palmettos were by far the most beautiful trees he had ever seen. Their long, swaying fronds looked like a million fingers in the sky pointing in every direction.

"As soon as we stop long enough in one place," he said to the other little boy, "let's climb all the way up one of those tall straight trees. We'll be able to see all of Florida from the top."

The other boy agreed. The motion of the horse

made him sleepy and he closed his eyes. But Little Owl continued to look about; he was too excited to sleep.

They came to a wet stretch on the trail. Other travelers before them had thrown several logs across it. While the horses stood still, swishing their tails, the men added a few more logs and some branches to make the crossing more comfortable for those on foot. When they started up again where the trail was drier, a flock of white egrets were frightened by the noise and took off in a snowy cloud, vanishing into the green brush. Little Owl watched them till they were out of sight. He had never before seen birds so white or so many birds all at once.

As they drew near a woody stretch, Little Owl saw a flock of parrots. From a distance they looked like bright green-and-yellow falling leaves. It was only when they were closer that the boy realized they were birds, and his mouth opened in wonder. Here and there in the watery swamp he

saw a heron standing motionless on one long leg, the other tucked under it, as it watched the people on the trail. After a moment or two the heron went back to its never-ending job of feeding. First it peered into the water with head cocked to one side. Then in plunged its bill and head, and up it came with a silvery fish struggling in the pincerlike bill.

Little Owl looked down into the shallow water, covered with lilies and broad round leaves, and was surprised to see little purple gallinules tripping merrily on their long toes over the leaves and twigs on top of the water. He wished he had long toes like that, so he would not sink into the water when he walked in a swamp.

The horses plodded on and were soon near the front of the line, where the men marched.

"Do you know this trail?" the boy heard his uncle ask the old Negro who was their guide. The Negro had escaped from slavery many years before. Then he had returned to Georgia to take his son, who was a slave on a cotton plantation, and his son's children back with him to Florida. His son had not been able to escape, but the old man had succeeded in getting away again, with a small grandson. He walked alongside the *miko* with the child on his shoulders. The old man wore a bright calico shirt and a tattered pair of dark pants. His grandson wore only a long bright-colored shirt.

It is because he has no wife that he carries the child, Little Owl thought. An Indian father carried his child only in a great emergency. Otherwise, the mother always carried the children.

The Negro guide placed his grandchild on a pack horse next to Little Owl's horse. "I know the way," the Negro said, straightening his tired back and speaking slowly in Creek. His voice was deep and very different from the even voices of the Indians. "I have been here before. We will soon come to a lake." The men quickened their pace and were soon too far ahead of the horses for Little Owl to hear their talk.

Owl looked about him again. The curly-haired grandson of the Negro guide was comfortable. He had closed his eyes and was falling asleep. The sloshing of the horses in the wet grass seemed to come from far away. Little Owl closed his eyes too, and was soon asleep.

He awakened in his mother's arms. She was lifting him down. As he opened his eyes, the first thing he saw was blue water stretching away to meet blue sky in the distance. The sky seemed to be under him, upside down. This must be the lake the old guide had spoken of, Little Owl thought. It was a large lake; he could not even see its far shore. He slid down from his mother's arms and ran to the water's edge.

People spread around him. Women slipped burden baskets off their shoulders, stretched, and arched their tired backs. Owl watched for his mother's nod of permission to jump into the water. She came over to where he stood, took his hand, and waded in with him.

"Are we going to camp here, Mother?" the

boy asked hopefully. He had already spotted a palmetto tree nearby and wanted to climb it. It was not as tall as those he had seen along the trail, but it would be good enough to practice on, he thought.

Mother was not sure. She looked around and then down at the surface of the water. "It would be safer to camp in the woods," she said. "We might stay here for a few days to rest and clean up. The lake is full of fish."

At the mention of fish, the boy let go his mother's hand and ran back to her burden basket. He got his own bone fishhook and a line of twisted fiber she had made for him before they left home. He tied one end of the line to the belt of his breechcloth. Mother took a slice of raw fish she had saved the night before and put the bait on the hook, and Owl threw his line into the water.

Already several older boys had waded in. Some held fishing lines. Others had cut poles and tied their lines to them. The fish were biting as fast as

the young fishermen could cast their lines. Little
Owl's luck was equally good. Almost at once he
felt a tug on his line and pulled in a fair-sized fish.
He swung it onto the bank and Mother took it off

the hook and put on another piece of bait. Again
Owl tossed in his line and pulled it taut. Meantime, Mother cut the fish he had caught, cleaned
it, and gave the boy a slice to chew.

Little Owl trembled with excitement. Never before had he caught fish so fast. Again he felt a tugging on his line and he quickly pulled it in with another fish. The second fish was even bigger. Mother let it struggle in the sand while she finished slicing the first fish. Then she cleaned and sliced the second. By that time Owl had caught a third fish.

He wanted to cast his line again, but his mother held him back. "Enough, son," she said. "We have enough for today. Tomorrow you will fish some more. If there is too much, the fish will spoil."

Little Owl would have liked to keep on fishing, but he could not disobey his mother. It was not the way of Indians to kill more than they could eat. As he slowly wound his line on a little stick, he watched the other boys still fishing. They had large families and needed many fish. Owl wished his mother had a few more people to feed, so he would not have to stop.

Mother had spread out the thin slices of fish on palmetto fronds, and Little Owl hurriedly sat down beside her to eat. As he ate, he fanned the flies from the food with another palm leaf. The fish tasted sweet and cool. Those who were not fishing sat on the sand eating slices of raw fish. There was no time to make fires and broil the fish or, better still, make a fish stew, which they would have preferred.

Mother spread out slices of fish to dry in the hot sun and then waded into the water with Little Owl. He wanted to learn to swim so Mother held him while he paddled about, churning the water with his arms and legs. Suddenly Mother let go of him and Little Owl went under. He struggled like a puppy and came up coughing and shaking the water out of his hair. He looked so funny that Mother began to laugh, and the boy laughed too.

Several men and older boys picked up their guns and their bows and arrows and turned to the woods. "The men are going to look for deer,"

Mother said. "Maybe we shall stay here for a while. Go and see what they are saying."

Owl was anxious now to climb the palmetto. He rubbed his arms and legs dry with his hands, put on his breechcloth, and went over to where his uncle and several other men sat talking.

"This is a good camp," he heard the *miko* say. "Plenty of wood and good water. Plenty of fish. Good hunting in the woods."

"It is a good place for a village," the medicine man said. "Let us remain here."

"It is good," the Negro guide agreed. "It may be safe for you here. But I must go on. My people would not be safe here, because we are too near the United States. The Spanish own these lands, but they are not strong enough to protect us against the slave traders from the United States. The planters of the South need many slaves to work their cotton plantations. Now that a law has been passed and slaves can no longer be brought from Africa, they will hunt even harder for escaped slaves—for us. So none of my people are safe unless we can disappear into the Florida jungles and swamps."

"What happened to the people who lived here before?" a young man asked. "We saw many ruins of villages along the trail."

"It is said there were many tribes when the Spanish conquerors came about three hundred years ago. The white man has killed off most of them. Many died of diseases. Some moved to the swamps and still live there. I know some who call themselves Calusa. It is also said that ancient tribes of Indians here in Florida built mounds many years ago where they buried their dead. I have seen some of these mounds south of here."

"Where do your people live now—the ones who escaped captivity?" the *miko* asked.

"In the swamps, mostly," the old man said. "My people have learned to build houses—chickees, they are called—on dry spots in the swamps. They live together in small villages. We are farmers. Some Indians have built villages near us. We trade with them. That is where I learned to speak your language."

"You speak it well," the *miko* said.

"I like to speak it," the old guide replied. "Your people in the swamps are our friends. Together we have fought the slave traders."

"You have guided us well and we want to remain here," the *miko* said. "Stay with us. We will be your friends too."

"Of this I am glad," the old man answered. "Our men are not great warriors like your people. We are farmers. But we are learning how to fight."

"Our women and children are tired," a man said. "We have gone far already. Our feet are sore. Some of the children are ill. This place will be our new home."

"I cannot remain here with you," the old man repeated. "I and my people are safe only in the swamps, where we can hide from the slave hunters." He stood up. He patted Little Owl, who had sat close to him listening to the men's talk. Then he picked up his grandchild and started for the trail.

Everyone else stood up to watch him go. Owl's mother ran up to the old man and put a few slices of the fresh fish, wrapped in a palmetto leaf, into his bundle. No one spoke, since the Indians have no word in their language for good-by. But their brown eyes, full of friendship, were an unspoken farewell. They stood in silence till the old man and the little boy disappeared around a bend in the trail.

Seeing everyone busy watching them, Little Owl thought this was a good time to slip away to the palmetto tree he wanted to climb. The tree looked even taller now that he stood under it. He had to tilt his head back to see all the way up the gray-brown trunk to the top. Little Owl took off his moccasins and began to climb, pressing his bare toes against the rough gray trunk. But he did not get far. He could get no hold for his arms or his feet. His chest was scratched by the rough ridges as he hugged the tree trunk. He had to rub it to keep it from smarting. Finally he gave up and dropped to the ground.

As he turned away from the palm tree, Little Owl was not too disappointed for he had seen something else, while climbing, that drew his interest. He slowly walked over to where two older boys were crouching on the ground, their breechcloths dragging in the wet grass. The bigger boy had a large ornament made of a clamshell on his chest. The other had two white feathers in his hair. They were watching something in a mudhole, near a clump of twisted cypress roots.

At first it seemed to Owl that the thing was a log—a piece of brown driftwood as long as himself. Suddenly it moved ever so slightly and Little Owl's lips formed the word, "*Allapatta!*" (Alligator.) He had seen an alligator only once before, a few days ago, in another swamp. Mother had pointed to the creature and said, "Be careful. This is an alligator. It has a mouth full of sharp teeth. An alligator is dangerous."

The alligator raised its head a half finger's length out of the water, till its long pointed snout stuck out. Its eyelids lifted and drooped shut again, as the head sank back into the warm brown water.

Owl edged closer, watching. Clamshell-necklace had a spear with him. He was holding it low, balancing it on the palm of his right hand, ready to strike. The other boy, Two-plumes, was aiming an arrow at the alligator. Owl held his breath, afraid to move and disturb the hunt.

The boys released their weapons at the same moment. The arrow glanced off the alligator's thick hide and sank into the muddy water, but the spear hit its mark and stuck in the alligator's side. The wounded creature plunged away through the water, dragging the spear, and a crimson streak spread after it.

Clamshell-necklace waded into the water; he did not want to lose his spear. Little Owl had seen him hammering the spear point out of a large nail. It had taken Clamshell-necklace a whole day to make it and another two days to whittle a long pole for the shaft. After the alligator had lashed about for a while, it became still. Clamshell-necklace waded farther out into the water, caught the handle of his spear, and began to drag the alligator to shore.

Then something else happened. Later, when Mother asked him to tell her all about it, Little Owl could not remember the details; it was too sudden. He did not even have time to be frightened. A big furry animal suddenly came in sight among the pines; the next moment it was up on its hind legs, sniffing the air. It scratched its light-colored belly with its front paws. Then it turned its head toward the boys and bared its sharp teeth in a snarl. It was a bear! Owl had never seen a live bear before, but he had seen hunters wearing bearskins during the Bear Dances and he knew that bears were dangerous. His mother had told him so. When she wanted him to stay close to the camp, she always said, "Don't wander off into the woods. There might be bears."

As he recalled Mother's words, Little Owl shouted a warning at the top of his lungs. "Oh-la, oh-la. B-bear!"

The bear moved fast toward Two-plumes, but Two-plumes' arrow flew even faster—right into the bear's belly. Mad with pain, the lumbering animal lunged forward. Two-plumes had already reached for another arrow and was running toward Owl. He let go with the second arrow, which pierced the bear's chest. Then Two-plumes picked up Little Owl and ran. After taking a few more steps, the bear fell.

Clamshell-necklace had looked up when Owl yelled his warning. He left his spear in the alligator and ran after Two-plumes.

Everyone in camp was already alerted, for they had all heard Little Owl's shout.

"We will call your son Asi-oh-la (Osceola)," the *miko* said to Mother later. "He has a good strong voice. When he gets a little older, we will let him be the crier at the men's ceremonies."

Little Owl's eyes sparkled with pleasure because the *miko* had given him a new name. Now his mother could drop his baby name. In an instant he had run over near the *miko* and in his loudest voice was shouting, "Asi-oh-la!" He had heard other boys shout this while serving the men with *asi* at ceremonies, a special black drink made of boiled herbs. "Asi-oh-la!" His clear, strong voice echoed over the lake, and everyone laughed happily.

"Let us make this our home," Two-plumes' mother said. "We will have good luck here."

"Come, Osceola," Mother said, proudly calling the boy by his new name. "We must make a shelter for the night."

2

THE CHICKEES

EVERY night, long after the children had crawled into the hastily built shelters to sleep, the men and women talked around the campfires about building new homes. All the people in the village always talked things over together and did what the majority wanted. The *miko*, whom the others had elected, saw to that. Each woman had already chosen a place near her relatives, where she wanted her new home. Here she had built a temporary shelter of brush and palmetto leaves. The women were particularly anxious for the men to help in building the new homes, because they hoped to settle here and they wanted sturdy buildings. The men would have to cut the heavy logs that were needed, but the women could chop down the palmetto leaves for the thatching.

These homes were to be very different from the bark-covered wigwams they had left behind them in Georgia. There a home had to be warm as well as rainproof. Here, they were told, the winters were so mild that no one had to worry about the cold. The dew was heavy in the evening and everything got damp, but the hot sun soon dried things out in the morning. The people had also heard that although the winters were dry there would be ample rain in late spring and summer.

The women liked the open houses, or chickees,

they had seen along the trail. A chickee had no walls, just a floor and a peaked roof. The floor was raised up on poles, so it would be dry even when the ground was wet. These open houses would always be cool and light, unlike the dark wigwams in Georgia.

Osceola and his mother shared their shelter with Turkey-wing. She was the oldest daughter of Mother's sister. Turkey-wing had two brothers and a little sister, and so her family's small shelter would have been too crowded if she had stayed there.

Osceola, his mother, and Turkey-wing were up early to start work on a small chickee. Mother was planning to build the chickee right next to her sister's. Back in Georgia, Turkey-wing had always taken care of the two children, Osceola and her own little sister Red-wing. But Turkey-wing had grown tall now and could help with the chickee. She and Mother decided that Osceola would have to take care of Red-wing, while the two of them went off in search of poles and palmetto leaves.

Osceola was disappointed. He would have liked to go to the woods with them, to help. However, Mother was using the only large metal knife they owned, so there would have been little chance for him to do any real work. Being an Indian boy, he thought of carrying wood as women's work. To work with a knife or a bow and arrow—or gun— was men's work. Since he could not do men's work this morning, Osceola went to play with Red-wing.

The little girl was chewing on a piece of baked fish. She was so happy to see Osceola that she gave him the whole slice of fish. Then she pulled a cornhusk doll from a basket, shook out the creases in its buckskin skirt and cape, and was ready to play house. Osceola had an idea. "We will build a house like the ones everyone is building now," he said.

"Chickee," said Red-wing.

She had heard her father and mother talking
about building their new house. Several men and
boys had gone back to the woods at dawn to cut

more trees for chickees. Now the children watched
Mother and Turkey-wing preparing four large
palmettos for her chickee. They picked up some

twigs and began to peel the bark off with their fingernails and their sharp teeth to make a toy chickee.

The sun was high when the men returned from the woods. They drove the smooth poles into the ground so that they were straight and firm. Then they cut deep notches in the poles about three feet from the ground. Crosspieces were laid in these notches from one upright to the next; they were fitted firmly into the notches and tied to the uprights with fiber rope so they could not slip out. Thin poles were laid across the square made by these crosspieces. Now the new chickee had a floor.

Osceola and Red-wing did not get around to building their toy chickee after all. They finished peeling the bark off a few twigs but dropped them when they saw that they could run under the crosspieces laid for the floors of the new houses. They raced back and forth under them, bending low like hunters speeding through the woods.

"I am glad the children like it so well here," they heard a woman say to Mother, as they dashed under her chickee. "I was afraid they would not like it in Florida. My husband said he would rather fight the palefaces than leave our homeland and find that our children were unhappy."

But despite this reassurance Mother called the children to help her. She did not want them to get in people's way, so she found work for them to do on the chickee. They set to with a will. This was better than building a toy house. Osceola felt he was really growing up, building his own chickee.

After the men had finished laying the floor, they stood on it and raised four heavy poles for the roof. The poles rested on the four uprights. Other shorter poles were raised from the uprights to support the slanting roof. The boys crisscrossed the frame with slender poles and tied them securely to the heavy posts.

The children took the palmetto leaves which Mother and Turkey-wing had brought from the

woods and handed them up to the boys. The men and boys tied the end of each frond to the thin poles, placing the leaves in a row, one next to the other. After they finished one layer, they put another layer higher up and overlapping the first, and then still another, until the fronds were almost used up. Mother and Turkey-wing hurried to the woods and were soon back with more palmetto leaves. While they were gone, the children kept on helping the men.

After several layers of palm leaves had been laid, the children, who were on the inside, could not see any light at all through the roof. Now it would be rainproof. Mother's chickee was finished.

Red-wing's mother called the children to help her and Turkey-wing now. The frame of their chickee had six upright poles so that it would be big enough for the two parents and their four children. Red-wing's mother had also cut down palmetto leaves. While she was in the woods getting more, the children handed the fronds to the men.

The children could still see specks of light through the roof when they looked up from the floor of the chickee. They needed more leaves, but it was getting late and Red-wing's mother did not want to go back to the woods. Like everyone else, she was tired. They decided to finish the work the following day. The sky was clear. There would be no rain that night, and they were getting used to the heavy dew that covered everything after sunset.

Meantime, the people whose chickees were finished, or almost finished, unpacked the burden baskets and stowed their blankets, pots, and bowls in their new homes. Osceola's mother hung their buckskin blanket on one of the crosspieces under her new roof. On the other she hung the shiny alligator skin Two-plumes had given Osceola a few days after he had speared the alligator. She balanced her burden basket between two of the poles overhead and put Osceola's fishing pole up there also. On the floor she laid the bearskin which Clamshell-necklace's mother had tanned and given to Osceola to thank him for his timely warning. It covered almost the entire floor of the small chickee. The chickee looked neat. It smelled of green wood and palm leaves and freshly tanned skin.

"This is the best house we ever had, Mother," Osceola said. He had lifted Red-wing up into the chickee and both were sitting on the new floor. "And I helped build it."

"There is still light enough for fishing," Mother suggested. "Take your line."

When it came to fishing, Osceola did not care how tired he was. He reached for his fishing pole at once, but then his eyes fell on Red-wing. He could not take her with him. The boys at the lake would laugh at him. Only girls took care of babies. He looked for Turkey-wing and saw that she was busy unpacking. Mother was going into a neighbor's chickee. So he would have to wait.

Several other women and the medicine man had gathered at the neighbor's chickee because there was a sick baby. The heat and strain of the march had evidently been too much for the little girl. She had lost weight and felt hot all over. The men had helped the baby's parents with their small chickee. Now mother and baby were resting comfortably on a bed of Spanish moss. The baby had nursed well that day for the first time in several days and had slept well.

The night before, the little girl's grandmother had picked some herbs near the lake. These she boiled in water and gave the medicine to the mother and baby to drink. The medicine man had sung a few special songs which he knew would please the spirits. These good spirits would then chase away the evil spirit that caused the illness and the baby would get well. To make sure that the evil spirit would not give the baby the sickness again, its grandmother renamed the little girl

Clearwater, after the lake where they had just settled. The new name would deceive the evil spirit. Now the women were bringing the baby presents to celebrate its getting a new name: a few beads, a piece of buckskin, a tiny pair of moccasins.

Red-wing's mother gave the baby the nicest gift of all—Red-wing's buckskin blanket, which all her other babies had used, too. All her babies had been healthy. None had died. Everyone was sure that the blanket of these healthy children would have the power to keep Clearwater healthy, too. They threw away the baby's old blanket so no other baby would ever use it and get sick.

Mother had told Osceola that the naming ceremony would be very short. The boy waited impatiently, hoping it would not get too dark before he reached the lake. At last he saw his mother coming from the other chickee. Red-wing's mother was with her, and Osceola handed the child over to her.

Osceola hesitated at the top of the steps of his chickee. There were three of them—three slender cross poles tied to two heavy upright poles which had been driven into the ground. Osceola had clambered up the steps earlier, but then both his hands were free. Now, with his fishing pole in one hand and the fish basket in the other, the little boy hesitated. He looked about to make sure no one was watching him. Then he jumped, landed safely, and set off to the lake.

Several boys were still fishing. Clamshell-necklace and Two-plumes called Osceola over to their fishing place. "Stay with us, Younger Brother," they said. "The fish are biting well. We will help you take the fish off your hook."

"Where were you this morning?" Two-plumes asked. "We came here early before the camp awoke and caught fresh fish for the morning meal."

The little boy was ashamed to tell them that he had had to take care of a baby, yet he felt he should explain why he had not gone fishing. He was silent for a while, thinking over the day's events. Then he said modestly, "I helped my mother build a house. The women are now busy building a small cooking hut. And I am going to get enough fish for Mother and Mother's sister's family. They are a large family." He did not want to tell the boys that he needed only one fish. He spread out the fingers of his right hand and held up three of his left to show how many people he had to provide for. He would have to fish for a long time.

"We need a lot of fish too. My mother will dry some of the fish we catch," Two-plumes said. "We need fish oil for stews."

Soon each of the three boys had hooked a number of fish. Clamshell-necklace said, "We all have enough now." He and Two-plumes helped Osceola carry his heavy basket of fish to his new chickee.

The women were crowding around their cook-

ing huts, which had no floors. The thatched roof
of each rested on four poles driven into the
ground. In the center was a large fire pit.

Already the smell of fish stew was in the air.
In her cooking hut Mother was fanning the small
fire. A large pot of stew steamed on a hook over

the fire and Turkey-wing was stirring the stew with a large stirring paddle. Her mother was busy finishing a large mat for their chickee. Red-wing sat on the floor nearby stirring with a toy paddle in a little clay pot. She was playing house, her favorite game. She fed her doll with a small wooden spoon just like the large one her father had carved for dishing out stew and corn mush.

Mother took Osceola's fish basket. She slashed each fish in two, leaving the tails uncut. Then she cleaned and scraped the fish, wrapped one in a large leaf for the morning meal, and hung the rest to dry.

Through the trees the sun had set over the lake. The sky was still tinted red from the sunset. Now it darkened to purple with deep purple patches where the clouds were. Except for the small fires in the cooking huts, darkness was closing in over the camp. Osceola quickly sat down beside Turkey-wing. He did not want anyone to think he was afraid of the dark, but he felt more comfortable near Mother or Turkey-wing. He picked up his spoon and held it, ready for the fish stew.

All over the new village shadows moved about the glowing cooking fires. People were enjoying the evening meal and the quiet. A man brought out a drum and began a low beat. Some of the other men sat quietly listening to the drum; others were talking to each other. The women were sewing, mending, or weaving mats. Everyone felt happy and safe.

Mothers got up from the fires to lead their children to the chickees to sleep. It was getting colder, and the children hung back, edging closer to the fires.

"We will have to put more thatching on our roofs," someone said.

"They will do for a while," a man answered. "We need canoes now. Canoes will help us to get to know this land better, and some of us want to go out fishing on this lake. We could also use new nets. We must make some."

Clearwater's father had caught a big turtle that day and he thought everyone would enjoy the turtle steaks. Clearwater's mother had sliced and pounded them thin. She had broiled them on heated stones and was now passing thin slices of turtle steak around for a treat. People dipped the meat into a salty paste made of wood ashes and ate the pale turtle meat with pleasure. It was not as tasty or tender as regular meat and fish, but it was a new food—a good thing to know about in an emergency.

"We will try to make a new kind of bread to-morrow," a woman said. "The Negro guide who left us told me about this. It will help tide us over till we get the ground cleared for cornfields, plant the seed, and harvest our crop."

They continued talking near the fires and listening to the beat of the drum.

Red-wing waked and called to her mother. She was not yet accustomed to sleeping in a house without walls and was afraid. She heard the rustle of the grass under the chickee and thought it was the "little people" from the Creek legends her mother had told her. "Look, Mother," she said, "the little forest people are under our chickee. They are dancing and beating a drum."

"The little people of the forest are kind," her mother reassured her. "If you dream of them, it is a good sign that they like you, and you need never be afraid of them. The little people are half as big as you are and they have lovely long hair and wear the finest buckskins. They are good little spirits.

"They will always help you find your way home. If a hunter loses his way they will help him, too. If he is tired or hurt, they will take him to the mountain caves where they live and will help him to regain his strength with corn and meat and good medicine. After he has rested and slept, they will guide him home. The little people are very kind to children, and no child need be afraid of being lost in the woods. The little people are sure to help him find his way home. So you see, daughter, there is nothing to fear."

Red-wing lay awake for a while, her head in her mother's lap, listening to the drum. Soon she closed her eyes and fell asleep.

3

THE DUGOUT

As USUAL, everyone was up at dawn. Although the newcomers had been in Florida for many weeks now and had lived in their new chickees for many days, there was still much to be done.

Just at daybreak, Turkey-wing brought Red-wing to Osceola's chickee and placed her on the bearskin near the boy.

Osceola looked at his mother, hoping that he would not have to play with Red-wing today. He had to think quickly. "Red-wing likes to play house, Mother," he said. "She likes babies. Now that Clearwater is well, Red-wing could take care of her, and Clearwater's mother could look after both of them."

Mother nodded. It was a good idea. It would make it possible for the boy to help in the woods. Quickly slipping on her buckskin cape, she took the extra fish she had saved from last night's meal, and went over to her neighbor's chickee, to ask her to take Red-wing and to make her a present of the fresh fish.

Osceola dressed quickly and tucked a small shell knife into the belt of his breechcloth. Two-plumes had made it for him from a piece of shell a few days before and it was quite sharp. He climbed down the ladder and followed his mother.

Clearwater's mother was glad to help her neighbors. The baby had recovered completely. She crawled on the chickee floor, gurgling happily. Ever since Clearwater had been wrapped in Red-wing's blanket, she had been thriving. Her mother looked upon Red-wing as a relative, with whom her child shared good luck.

She took Red-wing into her arms and sat down with her near Clearwater. "My daughter," she said, speaking to Clearwater, "here is Red-wing, your older sister, who is coming to look after you because she loves you, and she has brought us another gift, some good food. We thank her and her relatives."

Clearwater smiled, and Osceola jumped for joy. He was free at last. Now he would not have to do girls' work any more. Red-wing would stay with Clearwater's mother.

He followed Mother into the woods, where they set to work with hoes and knives, cutting and digging up coontie roots and stems. Other children carried them away and piled them near the water. Coontie, or Florida arrowroot, is a low-growing fernlike plant with long feathery leaves. It has a thick underground stem, from which coontie flour is made. Turkey-wing and her friends scrubbed stems and roots in the water till they were free of

earth and pebbles. Then they spread the knotted gray-brown stems to dry in the sun. When they had enough, the women tied them into bundles and carried them to the village with the help of the children.

There everyone set to work, pounding the coontie into pulp with flat stones and wooden clubs. The women had already tied racks between posts. Now they put the pounded roots into the top rack, which was made of a mat, and poured water over the pulpy mass. As the water seeped through the pulp it dissolved the starch in the roots, and the liquid drained through the mat to the rack below, which was made of watertight buckskin. There the liquid was left for a few days.

As the mixture thickened, a deep layer of fine powder settled on the bottom of the buckskin rack. This the women scooped up and spread on a mat in the sun to dry. It dried into a yellowish flour, finer than corn meal. The women rubbed it between their fingers and decided that they would bake bread from this new flour that very night.

The men, in the meantime, were busy making dugout canoes out of cypress logs which they had rolled down to the beach soon after settling in the new village. They had been fortunate in finding trees that had been blown down in storms and were now dry. These cypress trunks would make good canoes. The men formed two groups and each group set to work on one trunk, cutting off the branches and removing the bark. They threw burning embers on the logs. As the wood charred, they scraped it away with sharp metal adzes. It was not long before the dugouts began to take shape.

The boys ran errands for the men. They fetched water to drink and brought them food when they grew hungry. They carried the dry chips to the cooking huts for firewood. The men worked without stopping. Even the hot midday sun failed to stop them. They twisted bands of palmetto fronds about their heads for shade and continued working.

What they wanted to make were dugouts that could be used in shallow as well as deep water. They knew that most of their canoeing would be in shallow water. But how wide and how deep should these canoes be? They talked and argued. Each man told about his experiences with canoes and said what he thought an all-purpose canoe should be like. None of them had ever made such a canoe before.

Help came from a stranger. A canoe came gliding toward them around a bend in the shore of the lake. It was almost like a dream, when someone's wish is fulfilled by magic. No one dared look at the man beside him for fear that he was the only one dreaming or, as the Indians would say, seeing a vision. So each man stared at the canoe and at the tall, bronzed man who stood erect in the bow. The tall stranger held a long pole in his hands. He thrust the pole into the water and leaned against it, and the canoe shot forward.

The man's costume was the most beautiful the

newcomers had ever seen. Made of trade cotton cloth, the shirt was full, with long sleeves gathered in tight bands at his wrists. He wore a bright kerchief around his neck and a turban on his head. On his chest hung several wide plates of hammered silver shaped like half moons and glistening in the sun. His breechcloth, also of cotton, was fringed, the end reaching just below his knees.

The stranger must have seen the wonder in the men's faces and realized that they were only curious, not hostile. Once again he leaned heavily against the pole, and the canoe shot forward and glided lightly into their midst. In the bottom of the canoe sat a little boy, dressed like his father. He remained seated while his father jumped out of the canoe into the water and held the canoe by a rope fastened to the bow.

To everyone's amazement, the stranger spoke to them in Creek—their own language. "I come from a lake to the south," he said, indicating the direction by turning his head. "This is my son.

We are Creek too. My parents came here, just as you have done. They came from a place the white settlers called South Carolina. But I was born in Florida, a day's journey from here."

"Your canoe has caught our eyes," the *miko* said. "It moves fast."

"These lakes are not deep," the stranger told them. "You need a canoe that does not fetch too much water. That is why I made my canoe wide and shallow. You can use your paddle in the middle of the lake, where it is deeper. But here, near the shores, a pole is better. I carry both."

"You are wise," the *miko* said.

"I am a Creek too," the stranger said, accepting his praise but politely including everyone else in the compliment. "My parents used to tell me that their homeland had mountains and was not as flat as Florida. I have never seen mountains."

"We like it here," one of the men said. "This homeland of yours is full of beauty and of sunshine. There is plenty of game. We are making it our home."

The stranger's son lifted a basket from the canoe and put it down on the beach. The basket was his responsibility. But he gave the gun which he picked up from the canoe to his father. The new settlers crowded around to admire it.

"We get these in trade with the Spanish," the stranger explained. "We also trade for knives and good metal pots. I used a bow and arrow when I was a boy, but now we get guns and powder in trade for our furs. Many of us have guns now."

"Help us make a canoe like yours," the *miko* said, "and we will go with you. Perhaps we could trade too. We do not have many buckskins now, but we will hunt. Our women tan skins well. Right now we need knives even more than guns."

"The Spanish want the furs of the otter and raccoon and the feathers of birds," the stranger said.

"Do they wear feathers in war?" a man asked.

"No. They wear feathers only for festivals. The Spanish are not at war with the Indians. They want to live with us in peace."

The stranger's canoe was empty now, and the men lifted it gently and turned it over to see how it was shaped. Each man looked it over with great care, so its lines would remain in his memory.

Now they were ready to go to work again on their own dugouts. The stranger pulled his long knife from its sheath and fell to work with them. He showed them just how much the sides should be rounded and how to shape the bottom of the dugout so it would be almost flat. The front of the canoe must come to a point and curve upward so it would rise out of the water. Now that they all saw how to shape a canoe the men worked quickly. The stranger worked first with one group, then with the other, showing the men how to shape the log.

Even after the sun had set, the men were still chipping away at the canoes. But when dusk fell they had to quit.

The strangers were welcomed into the village by the women. "Is your mother Creek too?" one woman asked the boy.

"We are all Creek," the boy said, "but everyone calls us Seminole. And my name is Tigertail."

"I have heard the word *Seminole* before,"

Osceola's mother said. "It means people who go to another country. We must now be called Seminole like yourself."

The strangers were to be the guests of the *miko*, whose wife had a special treat for them. That morning, while gathering firewood, her daughter had seen a turtle laying eggs. When she first saw

it, the turtle had already laid a layer of eggs in a mound of dead leaves near an old tree stump. The girl watched the turtle lay a second layer. With its hind feet and claws it threw leaves over the layer till the eggs were well covered and looked like a little mound of dead leaves. When the turtle went away, the girl took off her cape and spread it on the ground. She brushed away the leaves and carefully piled the round, soft-shelled eggs in it. Then she carried them home.

Her mother pinched a tiny hole in one egg and the girl sipped the liquid and the tasty yolk. The turtle egg had a fishy flavor but she liked it. She and her mother wrapped the eggs in leaves before putting them into hot ashes to bake. They were to be a special treat for the men when they returned from the beach. They turned out to be a special treat for the strangers, too, who said they were very fond of turtle eggs.

There was another treat for everyone. The women had made bread from the coontie flour. They mixed the coontie flour with water, added some berries and fat, and baked the mixture. The bread was orange in color and was very tasty.

Everyone liked the new bread and ate it with the fish stew.

The chief lit his pipe and handed it to the tall stranger, who took a few puffs and passed it to the man on his left. After the day of activity the village was dark and quiet again. Children sat close to their mothers, as quiet as the grownups. The full moon was high in the sky and the children watched it move into a cloud. The night grew darker while the moon was hidden. The dark faces of the people were blotted out, and the children moved closer to their mothers and older sisters. Then the round, smiling face of the moon came out again and the children could see the faces close to them once more. The boys carried in several heavy dry logs and soon had a large campfire blazing.

Ever since he had first seen the stranger poling his canoe, Osceola had wanted to tell his mother about poling and how swiftly the canoe had moved. He thought he would show her, now that the moon and the fire made everything bright. He rose and picked up his fishing pole. Standing sideways to the fire, he placed the end of the pole down at his side. His legs astride, he leaned against the pole, twisting his body with the effort of his make-believe push against the bottom of the lake. He raised his pole just above the ground, as the stranger had raised his just above the surface of the water, and waited, as the stranger had waited, for the canoe to glide forward. Again he pressed the pole into the ground and again raised it and waited for the glide.

This was a new sort of dance to the Creek. Tigertail, the stranger's son, knew how to pole. He stood up too. He did not have a pole, so he stretched his arms out to one side, making believe he had a pole in his hands. Several boys, some with fishing poles, some without, lined up behind Osceola and Tigertail and followed their motions.

A man brought his drum out of his chickee. He moved over to the side of the fire and began

to beat the drum to the rhythm of the boys' poling. "This is our first Florida dance," the *miko*
told the stranger.

Because this was just a dance following a feast
and not a ceremonial dance or a war dance, no
one sang. The faces of even the youngest dancers,
however, were very serious. The dance looked
simple—heel-and-toe, toe-and-heel, in rhythm
to the drumbeat. But it was not really as simple as
it looked. No one had rehearsed for this dance,
yet no one, not even the smallest boy, wanted to
make a mistake which might make people laugh
at him.

Now the girls and a few women were dancing
too. They did not join the line of men dancers
but formed a line of their own. Little Red-wing
was at the end of the line, behind Turkey-wing.
She followed Older Sister's steps closely. Like
Older Sister, Red-wing put her right toe forward
and let her entire weight fall back to one side as
she stepped on the heel of her left foot and bent

her left knee. She kept her arms motionless at her sides, swaying first to one side, then to the other in time with the drumbeat.

Osceola was concentrating just as hard in the line of boys. Their steps were a little different from the women's steps. Men liked to add variety to their dance steps. The step was toe-and-heel, heel-and-toe, but some of the older boys and men, who had more dancing experience, crossed their left foot over the right to make their dance step more imaginative. Then they crossed the right over the left on the next drumbeat. Other men and boys raised one knee and stood motionless for a beat. Still others tapped a heel slightly as they lowered it to the drumbeat.

The people were happy to see how much the dance pleased their guest. When the drummer stopped for a rest and everyone went back to his place by the fire, the stranger got up to do a dance in honor of his hosts. He went toward the chief's chickee and picked up his spear.

Tigertail sidled over to the drummer and asked permission to beat the drum. The drummer moved aside and the boy slipped into his place and sat cross-legged in front of the drum.

The tall stranger stood alone and still in the firelight. He had taken off his outer garment and stood naked except for his breechcloth. Then he turned sideways, slowly raised his long spear in

his right hand, and balanced it on his upturned right palm as though feeling its weight. Its length was greater than his height. The metal spearhead glistened in the firelight. Two long white feathers tied to the butt end of the pole fluttered in the air. The stranger knew that every eye was already upon him, yet he stood still, as though waiting for more attention.

89

Slowly, as Tigertail slapped the drum, his father raised his left arm till his forearm rested against his forehead. He looked long into the distance, as though spotting the deer he was about to kill. When at last he moved, it was done so swiftly that everyone in the audience started and sat up straight.

Still gripping his spear in his right hand, the dancer began to circle the fire, heel-and-toe, toe-and-heel, faster and faster till he was running. His upraised spear seemed glued to his hand. Faster and faster he ran, as Tigertail kept on drumming.

Suddenly the hunter fell back on his left heel and the drum stopped. Again he strained into the distance with his forearm over his eyes. The deer had evidently stopped running. Slowly the drum began to beat again and the hunter approached his prey with caution. Everyone in the audience held his breath for fear of betraying the hunter to the deer by a cough or a motion.

And then the hunter hurled his spear into the darkness!

With both hands free, he turned to the audience and began to prance about with joy over the successful hunt. In his joy and triumph, he twirled and twisted an imaginary spear over his head, making figures of eight in the air. The drum beat loudly, and one by one the men fell in line behind the dancer, twirling their imaginary spears in the air too, throwing them far into the dark, and prancing with joy as though they had struck the target.

Tigertail's arms ached and he fell back, away from the drum. The regular drummer picked up his rhythm and continued to beat till the men began to slow down with exhaustion. The drummer stopped. The dance was over.

"You have brought us much that is new," the *miko* said to the stranger. "We will return this visit soon. And now you and your son must rest. There are places for you in my chickee."

4

STILL ON THE MOVE

IT WAS now 1818 by the white man's count. Ten years had passed. For seventy years, Indians and Negroes had been moving into Florida. For the most part, the Negroes had come one by one after a desperate flight with the white men at their

heels till, exhausted, they reached the swamps—
and freedom from slavery. Most of the Indian
groups had been forced out of their homelands in
the Southeast by white settlers. They trekked into
Florida with their families, bringing as many of
their possessions as they could and as much of their
livestock as survived the long march. The number
of people in Florida began to increase again,
though it did not equal the large population of
the early days before the Spanish conquest. The
Seminole population was nearing five thousand
now.

Each group tried to build its village in a place
where they would be as comfortable and safe as
possible. They all looked for a home near water,
since fishing was important; they also needed land
for cornfields and woods for hunting. They
avoided making their homes near the paths of
migration so they would be safer from the white
men. A few more groups settled near the village
where Osceola's people lived. Some were Negroes,

some Indians. They built similar chickees for themselves. They, too, learned to make coontie bread and to carve shallow dugouts that would take them through the swamps, lakes, and rivers.

The newcomers were friendly neighbors now. They traded with one another. They attended each other's feasts and ceremonies and they played games together. They came to think of themselves as one tribe—the Seminole. Thus a new tribe came into being, tied by common interests and a common love for their new country, and facing a common enemy, the white man.

All went well in the new land. The Seminole worked hard. There was ample food. They enjoyed good harvests. The cattle they brought with them from the United States thrived in the year-round green pastures and multiplied. The children grew taller than their parents. All enjoyed better health than they had ever had before.

In the warm, even climate everyone spent most of his time outdoors. The boys were free to roam

the woods for small game or to fish in their dugouts. They learned to take care of themselves and
felt safe in the swamps. It was not unusual for a
group of boys or even a single boy to go off in a
canoe and stay away for several days, exploring
or visiting neighboring villages. They came to
know the nearby lakes and rivers and connecting
waterways which the Indians had cleared. They
became familiar with the whole region around
their villages.

One afternoon, when all the men were away on
a hunt, several white men came to Osceola's village and demanded that the women tell them
where they would find the Negroes from a neighboring village. The Negroes had all disappeared.
The white men said these Negroes were their
slaves. "Tell us where they are, or we will burn
your chickees and cornfields to the ground," they
threatened.

The women said the Negroes were not slaves.
They and their families had been living in the

village for a long time and were free men now. They did not know where they had gone but would ask the men when they returned from the hunt. The white men said they would wait for the men to return. They sat down in the shade of a tree.

Secretly the women sent four of the boys to warn the men. Osceola and three other youths raced down trails well known to them and soon came upon the men. Several of them rushed back to camp and found the search party still under the tree, half dozing. Stealthily crawling behind them, the Seminole men plunged their long knives into the white men's backs.

The Seminole did not know how soon the slain men would be missed, but it seemed safest to make plans for moving at once. First they sent the boys in canoes to the neighboring Seminole and Negro villages to warn them of danger. Then they packed their belongings quickly. Several families set off in canoes. The rest, with their cattle and

horses, started overland toward a meeting place farther south which had been agreed upon.

Osceola proudly poled his own canoe, with his mother seated comfortably in the stern. He and the other boys were not too much upset by this new move. They knew where they were going and were glad of the chance to live in another place on this beautiful peninsula. In a canoe next to Osceola stood Two-plumes. He was still Osceola's closest friend and they always hunted and fished together. Clamshell-necklace had married a girl from across the lake and had gone to live with her people. Two-plumes was now a relative of Osceola as well as a friend, for he had married Turkey-wing. She and their two small children were in the canoe with him. Red-wing, who was as old now as Turkey-wing had been when they first moved to Florida, was traveling with the overland party, in order to help her parents with the livestock.

The canoe party journeyed south for several days, poling and paddling, paddling and poling. They left their lake, went up a small river, and carried the canoes over to another much larger lake. Now they felt safer. They camped, and waited for the overland parties to catch up with them.

At last the overland parties arrived. A good place, entirely surrounded by swamp, was chosen

for the new village. Again the men cut down palmettos for chickees and the women gathered palmetto leaves. Again the children helped. Osceola, who was now doing man's work, built his mother's small chickee.

After many days the new chickees were finished, the cooking huts set up, and small shelters made for the chickens and livestock. Once more the women built frames for making coontie flour and strung lines between the houses for drying fish and meat. Coontie bread would tide them over till cornfields were planted again and a crop harvested. The boys went fishing and the women began to hoe small patches for planting corn, beans, and pumpkins.

The alarm came sooner than they had expected, sent by Indian and Negro messengers. Although Florida still belonged to Spain, General Andrew Jackson and 3000 United States troops had invaded the peninsula. Jackson had all but wiped out the Creek population of Southern Georgia and he aimed to do the same to the Seminole of Florida.

"He is coming here to kill us all," the messengers cried.

The Seminole chiefs called upon all their braves to join in a war against the white men. The number of Seminole braves was relatively small, but they had one important advantage—they knew the country better than Jackson's men. So the

Seminole fought the same kind of war their ancestors had always fought—a guerrilla war. Braves in small groups raided and molested the troops. Boys, as well as men, took part in these raids, Osceola among them.

When Spain protested to the United States government about invading her possession, the United States agreed to buy Florida from Spain for five million dollars. In the treaty that covered this purchase, Spain asked that the people of Florida be accepted as citizens of the United States. The Federal government agreed to this, but the Indians and the Negroes of Florida were not considered citizens. They were people of a different color and a different way of living. In those days white men thought that people who were different from themselves were inferior and therefore not entitled to freedom and justice. So the fighting went on.

The treaty of 1823, which ended the first Seminole War, was not a very big victory for Jackson's forces. The Seminole did not leave Florida. They agreed to stay in the swamps provided the white settlers left them alone and did not search for Negro slaves among them, or ask them to move.

Things were quiet for the next few years. Once more the Seminole and the Negroes in the swamps were busy rebuilding homes and digging canals to connect the lakes so they could travel greater distances by canoe. They cleared patches of land for their cornfields and vegetable gardens and raised cattle in the good green pastures.

In May, 1830, President Jackson signed the Indian Removal Act. This came as another unexpected blow to the Seminole. Under this act all the Indians of the Southeast were to be moved across the Mississippi into Indian Territory. Immediately the white settlers of Florida began to demand that all the Seminole be moved too, but the Seminole refused to leave their homes.

Commissioners from the Federal government came to Florida to tell the Seminole that the land they would get in Indian Territory would be better than the Florida swamps. The Seminole did not trust the commissioners, but they finally agreed to send several chiefs to Indian Territory to look over the region the government planned to allot them and bring in their report. They promised to act in accordance with this report.

Seven Seminole chiefs, together with their agent, John Phagan, were taken by boat through the Gulf of Mexico to New Orleans. They sailed from New Orleans up the Mississippi and then up the Arkansas till they reached Fort Gibson in Indian Territory, now part of the State of Oklahoma. They looked over the western portion of the Creek Nation's land that was to be assigned to them and said that they liked it and would report this to their people back home.

But the government commissioners wanted more definite and speedier action. First they got the Creek to agree to take the Seminole, who had left them years before to migrate to Florida, back into the Creek Nation. The commissioners then showed this agreement to the Seminole delegates and urged them to sign the treaty agreeing to removal. They argued that the Seminole were not wanted in Florida, while here in Indian Territory they were. Land had been set aside for them. No white settler would be allowed to cross into their territory after they had moved. The Seminole chiefs argued that they were merely an investigating party and had no right to sign a treaty. But some of them finally gave in. In April, 1833, a few of the delegates signed a treaty, stating their willingness to be removed to Indian Territory.

When they returned to Florida, all the Seminole chiefs met in council, and the delegates reported what had taken place. Everyone was upset. "You had no power to commit us all to removal," the chiefs said. "We don't want to move." The Seminole urged John Phagan to call upon the commissioners in Washington and break the treaty, but Phagan refused to do this.

The treaty stated that the Seminole would have three years in which to get their property together and move out of Florida. But in the year 1835 the Seminole still had made no plans to move. The new Indian agent, Wiley Thompson, and several United States commissioners called the Indian chiefs together in May, 1835. Thompson laid the treaty before them and told them it was time they got ready to go. If they refused to, the United States government would send troops in to force them out. "When will you move?" Thompson asked.

The chiefs were silent. Suddenly Osceola, his eyes ablaze with anger, his silver ornaments glittering on his chest and arms, stepped boldly up. He pulled his long knife out and plunged the shiny blade right through the paper. "This," he said, "is our answer!"

Agent Thompson was taken aback. He had not expected this open declaration of war.

Osceola resumed his place among the group of

chiefs. He had evidently spoken for all of them. He was then only thirty-two years old, the youngest in the group.

Actually, very few definite facts are known about Osceola's life up to the time he stepped forward and faced Wiley Thompson and the commissioners. The Seminole had no written records of their own, and the records about the Seminole kept by the government show no interest in Osceola till he became a chief. We do know that he was born in about 1803 and came to Florida in about 1808. No one knows much about Osceola's father or mother. Some historians say that his grandfather or his great-grandfather was a white man. It is known, however, that his father was a Creek. Exactly how Osceola received his name is uncertain. The story about him in this book follows the few known facts. The rest has been pieced together from the migrations of the Creek into Florida and the way a Seminole boy usually grew up, received his name, and learned the skills necessary to care for himself and his family.

Thompson knew that Osceola's declaration was not a hasty one. And, having spoken for all, Osceola was the new war leader.

OSCEOLA

The white men noticed the stern faces of the chiefs. Their minds were made up and no one could change them. Mikanopi was their oldest and wisest peacetime chief. The Seminole thought of him as the *miko* of the tribe. Next to him stood Jumper, their leader in councils. Then came Coa

Coochee, or Wild Cat, as the white men called him. He was the son of King Philip, a chief of the St. Johns River region. Next to these stood several of the chiefs who had been to Oklahoma: Takos Emathla, Holati Emathla, and Holati's son Charley. These three were in favor of removal, because they felt it was no use trying to fight the greater forces of the white men.

Osceola's anger, now that he had spoken, subsided and gave way to determination. Another expression was on his face too, an expression of sadness. He had been raised here in Florida and he loved it. He had declared war, but not for the sake of personal glory, not to add more feathers to his hair for bravery. He was fighting for a home for himself and his people. He remembered the hardships, the labor of moving and setting up homes again and again, only to have to move again and again under the pressure of the white settlers.

He knew that destruction and suffering lay

ahead of the Seminole. When a whole people was on the run, no one, not even the smallest child, got enough rest or food or play. Everyone was always watching for an enemy who might be lurking behind a clump of tall grass, a bush, or a thick tree trunk—waiting to kill. One of their own people might betray them. A brave might get too much to drink from a white man and tell the hiding places of his people, the number of warriors, the names of the traders who sold them their guns and ammunition.

One day Osceola and the men from his village were away hunting. When they returned home they found their village deserted. A few women returned after dark from their hiding places in the swamps and told the story. Slave traders had caught several women and children who were working in the cornfields and had carried them off. The rest had slipped away.

The Seminole could no longer trust Charley Emathla, because he seemed friendly with the white men and was in favor of moving to Indian Territory. They decided to kill him so that he would not betray them. Now the Seminole had to leave their homes and hide in the depths of the swamps. Their cornfields and gardens had to be abandoned. Cattle were left behind. People had to stay hidden for days in the swamps, afraid to go out hunting, their clothing wet through and through. The boys were afraid to go fishing.

The United States government acted at once and sent troops after the Seminole, but the troops did not get very far. On their way to Ocala, then Fort King, Major Dade and his men were surrounded by Osceola's warriors and Negro allies and killed. Only three men escaped and lived to tell the tale. Thus, in 1835, began the second Seminole War. The Federal government then ordered General Thomas Jesup to direct an all-out campaign against the Seminole, and his troops began to move into Florida.

As soon as the Seminole saw the large troop

movements, Osceola ordered the women and children deeper into the swamps. In many cases they did not leave for the swamps fast enough and many saw their homes and cornfields going up in smoke. General Jesup burned everything in his path, hoping to starve the Seminole into submission.

The Seminole struck back. They lured small groups of soldiers into the swamps, ambushed and killed them, and got their guns and ammunition, which they needed badly. Spanish, French, and English pirates kept supplying the Seminole with ammunition, but there was always need for more.

The fighting went on for two years, till newspapers all over the United States set up a clamor to end the war. General Jesup, who had taken over command after several other generals had failed, decided to do something to end the war. Jesup tricked the Seminole chiefs. His lieutenant, under a white flag of truce, invited Osceola to General Jesup's headquarters at Fort King to discuss peace terms and the release of the Seminole warriors they were holding as prisoners. Osceola and Wild Cat came in good faith. As they entered Jesup's camp, the soldiers surrounded them. One of them hit Osceola on the head.

Osceola regained consciousness in the dark cell where the soldiers had thrown him. He tried vainly to lift his aching head from the floor. His arms and ankles were bound tightly and he could not move them. In the darkness, Osceola listened as the pain throbbed in his head. He heard no sound except his own breathing. He was alone.

His whole body felt so heavy that he thought bitterly he would have been unable to move even if they had not bound him.

He knew the Seminole would continue fighting, and he wondered what had happened to Wild Cat and whether he was in prison too.

He dozed off and dreamed of Lake Clearwater. He was a boy again, running to the water for a swim, but something held him back. He strained and strained to move. The water looked cool and clear, as he had always known it, while he felt hot all over. But his legs would not take him even one step. He awoke groaning and thirsty.

There was a light in the cell. Several soldiers stood over him, looking down at him. They untied his arms. "Promise us that you and your people will leave Florida, and we will set you free," one of them said in Seminole.

Osceola shut his eyes and turned his face away. He did not want to speak to a white man again. The men talked among themselves and left.

Osceola was left in the dark once more. He did not know how long he remained on the floor. At last the door opened and a soldier came in and gave him a cup of water and a piece of bread. He drank the water but could not eat the bread, because his throat hurt too much to swallow food.

He could not tell when it was day or night and soon lost track of time. One day the soldiers came to take him out. Osceola could not stand up by himself and a soldier had to hold him up. His throat had become inflamed and he had not been able to eat since his capture. The soldiers were watching him, Osceola noticed. He shut his eyes to blot out their faces. He kept his head lowered so they would not see the pain in his face. But it was good to feel the warmth of the sun.

Osceola knew they were taking him north, away from Florida, but he did not know the fort to which they brought him. It was Fort Moultrie in South Carolina. Again the soldiers left him in a dark cell. By this time Osceola did not care. He waited for death to stop the constant pain in his throat. He believed that after death he would be reunited with his mother and all his relatives who had died. Once more he would be with the many braves who had died at the hands of the white men. In that happy land where everyone lived forever, he would never suffer pain again. He would hunt and fish and play games. . . .

Osceola died in January, 1838, just a few months after his capture. The fighting in Florida continued.

A month before, General Jesup had played the same trick again and arrested old Chief Mikanopi and several subchiefs and warriors. He had asked them to come to talk about freeing Osceola. But even this did not end the war. The fighting continued under new chiefs, Alligator and Jumper. The Federal government finally gave in. In 1842, General W. J. Worth agreed to end the war and let several hundred Seminole remain in their hideouts in the swamps. He also promised to help those who wanted to move to Indian Territory.

The descendants of those people who remained in the Florida swamps are the Seminole we see in Florida today. There were only a few hundred left after the wars and the migration of 1842. The population has now grown to about eight hundred.

Some 3000 Seminole began to migrate to Indian Territory. First to migrate were Holati Emathla and his band. Holati, however, never reached the lands assigned to the Seminole between the Canadian River and its north fork. He died at Fort Gibson, Oklahoma.

As they were rounded up by the Federal troops, other groups of migrants got under way. They were first taken to New Orleans, where they waited for steamers to take them up the Mississippi and the Arkansas to Fort Gibson. From there they traveled overland to their new lands. The commissioners advised the Seminole to leave their household goods behind, because they wanted to

pack as many people as possible into the boats. The
Seminole were promised that they would be given
axes, hoes, and kettles when they reached Indian
Territory.

At New Orleans, while waiting for boats to
take them up the rivers, the Seminole lived in
crowded barracks. They were without guns and
could not hunt. Besides, troops watched them con-
stantly for fear they would run away. The food
they received was meager and they were not accustomed to it. So many of them fell sick and
many died.

Those who finally reached their lands in Indian Territory found Creek Indians already living there. The Creek refused to move, saying that
the government had given them the land first.
The Creek Indians also had Negro slaves and
some claimed that a few of the Negroes who
came with the Seminole belonged to them. The
poor, tired, starved Seminole refused to leave Fort
Gibson and move in among those "wild Indians,"

as they called the Creek. They did not want to become part of the Creek Nation. They wanted to live as a Seminole Nation and follow their own laws instead of those of the Creek.

They remained at Fort Gibson. The government rations, which cost about three cents a day per person, were poor, so the Seminole migrants were always hungry. Yet they preferred starvation to fighting with the Creek. Some Seminole moved a short distance away from the fort and settled among the Cherokee. Chief John Ross of the Cherokee, who with his people had only recently undergone the same exhausting migration, felt sorry for the Seminole and let them remain on Cherokee land. Unfortunately, the Seminole, although grateful to the Cherokee for this hospitality, were driven by hunger to kill Cherokee cattle to feed their families. Still John Ross refused to take action against them; he asked his people to wait till the Seminole difficulties were straightened out by further treaties.

A treaty was finally signed in 1845. The Creek agreed to set aside a tract of land for the Seminole, who were to govern themselves. They were to be a nation as before. Chief Mikanopi was again declared their *miko*.

In 1850, Wild Cat, who was not happy in Indian Territory, left for Mexico with his band to seek better living conditions and started a colony there.

The other Seminole, in the meantime, had spread throughout their new land in Indian Territory, building homes, clearing the ground for cornfields, planting rice in the wet places, and starting to breed cattle in the drier parts of their land. Government agents, experts in farming and cattle raising, were ready to teach them and help them get started. They still had occasional encounters with Creeks who refused to move, because they had lived on those lands before the Seminole came.

The final organizing of a Seminole government was further delayed by the Civil War, which split the Seminole Nation into two groups. One group, under Chief John Jumper, sided with the Confederates. The other group, under Chiefs Billy Bowlegs and John Chupco, were on the side of the Union. The Confederate commissioner, Albert Pike, urged Bowlegs and Chupco and their people to join the Confederates, but they refused. They left their homes and moved north to Kansas, where the Creek chief Opothleyahola, who was also on the Union side, welcomed them. They organized the Indian Home Guard Brigade of the Union Army. Both Seminole groups fought in the Civil War, on opposing sides. John Jumper was made a colonel in the Confederate army.

After the Civil War, on March 21, 1866, the chiefs signed a treaty to sell their lands to the United States for about $325,000. The price per acre was fifteen cents and the Seminole then owned over two million acres. With this money they were to buy 200,000 acres of land from the

Creek at fifty cents an acre. This treaty also re-
warded those Seminole who had fought for the
Union. Fifty thousand dollars was set aside for
the purpose of paying them small sums each year
in return for the losses they had to bear during the
Civil War, when they left their lands in Oklahoma. The Seminole who sided with the Confederates did not get anything for damages done to
their lands and homes.

However, after buying the land from the
Creek, the Seminole found that 200,000 acres of
land were not enough for their people and so they
bought another 175,000 acres from the Creek at
a dollar an acre. Now at last, with 375,000 acres
bought and paid for out of tribal funds, they were
a nation with sufficient territory.

But it was not till 1868 that the Seminole Nation was formally established, with a capital at
Wewoka in Oklahoma. They elected a *miko* by
majority vote. They had a subchief, a national
council of forty-two men, and a company of light-

horsemen. The Seminole Nation was divided into fourteen towns, or groups. Twelve of these towns were Seminole and two were made up of Negroes who had been freed. Each town sent three representatives to the national council. The light-horsemen were the Seminole policemen. They did such a fine job that the Seminole soon became known as the most peaceful and law-abiding Indian nation. Their newly elected chief, John F. Brown, governed them for over thirty peaceful years. The people worked hard and prospered.

In 1844, John F. Bemo, a Seminole, who had been educated by missionaries, came to Indian Territory with his wife and opened a school. Some years later they had three schools.

Real prosperity came to the Oklahoma Seminole in 1923, and with it world fame. In that year the Greater Seminole Oil Field near Wewoka began to operate. However, not all the Seminole became wealthy as a result of the discovery of oil. By 1923 only one fifth of their original land holdings remained in Seminole hands; they had lost the rest. What land they still had was divided into small parcels. So the income from the oil wells was divided among many Seminole.

Today the Seminole of Oklahoma are citizens of the United States. They still have a tribal government made up of a chief and a council of about thirty-six members from each of the twelve towns. The council still meets at Wewoka and it serves as adviser to the United States Indian Office on matters concerning the welfare of the Seminole people.

Half the Seminole living in Oklahoma today are still full-blooded Indians, many of whom have married their Creek neighbors. Of the other half, some have married white people and some Negroes. They still conduct ball games and dances, and the older people still observe some of the old tribal ceremonies.

5

SLOW—INDIAN VILLAGE

EVEN after the peace of 1842, after most of the
Seminole had been removed to Indian Territory,
the Florida Seminole were not left alone to enjoy
the peace they had fought for. They were still
molested by white men. The slavers needed Negro

labor and continued to search the Florida swamps for escaped slaves. They clashed with the Seminole, who refused to give up the Negroes. The slavers, however, did catch some Negroes and took them back to work on the cotton plantations. They kept complaining to the Federal government that the Seminole were helping their slaves to escape.

Once again the Federal government sent agents to induce the remaining Seminole to move out of Florida. The Seminole refused. The Federal agents brought in a group of Indian delegates from Indian Territory to tell these Seminole how good living conditions were there. The delegates refused to speak anything but the truth. They reported that conditions in Indian Territory were far from good. After months of work the Federal agents succeeded in removing fewer than fifty people, of whom seven died on the way to the West.

When they were not threatened by slavers, the

Seminole were harassed by white settlers. In 1855, surveyors came to the Big Cypress Swamp. A group of Seminole, under Chief Billy Bowlegs, watched the surveyors deliberately trample and destroy their cornfields, vegetables, and fruit trees. That night Billy Bowlegs and his warriors held a council and decided to act. They attacked the surveyors' camp at dawn and killed everyone in it, thus starting the third Seminole War.

This war continued for three years. Troops sent against the Seminole had to wade deep into the swamps to find them, for they never fought in the open. Their fighting now, almost twenty years later, followed the same pattern as it had in Osceola's day. They lured detachments of troops into the swamps. A quiet deserted swamp, with a small dry island in the middle where troops stopped to relax and rest, and dry their clothes, would suddenly resound with war whoops, as a swarm of yelling, war-painted Seminole descended upon them. Few of the troops escaped.

In 1858 the Federal government decided to give in; they offered the Seminole money to get out of Florida. Billy Bowlegs and one hundred and twenty-three men, women, and children agreed to leave Florida for Indian Territory. He was given a large sum of money for himself, each of his subchiefs received a thousand dollars, each brave five hundred, and each woman and child one hundred. Forty-one other Seminole, who had been captured by the troops, were forced to go West. One of them killed himself rather than leave Florida. But although all the Seminole were worn out with fighting, several hundred of them refused to leave their homeland.

After the fighting was over in 1858, the Federal government took stock of the expenses and the losses resulting from the three Seminole Wars. The United States had spent five million dollars in buying Florida from Spain. Over fifteen hundred men had been killed in the wars, and the total cost of the campaigns came to twenty million dollars. Despite this great outlay, the Federal government had achieved its goal only in part. It had rid Florida of most of its Indians, but about three hundred and fifty still remained in the swamps.

Today there are three Federal reservations in Florida for the Seminole. The reservations are called Dania, Brighton, and Big Cypress. All three are north of the Tamiami Trail. This is the famous highway which connects Miami on the Atlantic Coast with Tampa on the Gulf of Mexico.

This part of Florida is a wild grassy plain—a sea of grass called the Everglades. It is dotted with dwarf pine-like cypresses and mangrove swamps spread along the coast. Here and there small, dry islands covered with pines, palmettos, oaks, and shrubs rise above the swampy plains. There are still some wild animals left in the wooded areas: deer, bear, wildcats, foxes, rabbits, opossums, mink, raccoons, skunks, and squirrels. There are

SEMINOLE INDIAN
VILLAGES AND
RESERVATIONS

still many alligators in the swamps, as well as snakes, frogs, and large turtles. And there are fish in the rivers, lakes, and canals. Many Seminole are still hunters, trappers, fishermen, and farmers.

The Dania Reservation, just north of Miami, is the smallest of the three Seminole reservations. About sixty people live on it. They have about five hundred acres of grazing land, small gardens, and cornfields.

To the northwest of Lake Okeechobee is the Brighton Reservation. This has some thirty-six thousand acres of grazing land and a population of over two hundred. Cattle raising is their most important occupation.

The third, called the Big Cypress Reservation, is south of Lake Okeechobee and north of the Everglades National Park. Over one hundred Seminole live on its forty thousand acres.

The State of Florida had at first set aside a reservation for the Seminole in the Ten Thousand

Island region along the western coast. The reservation proved uninhabitable, since it was too wet and swampy for either farming or cattle raising. The Seminole were then offered another piece of land, near the Big Cypress Reservation. They have not settled there permanently, but they camp on it and use the land for grazing.

Cattle raising has become most important to the Seminole. Herds of short-legged, brown-and-white Herefords now roam the year-round range and thrive and fatten on its grass. The Seminole own several thousand head of these cattle. Brahman cattle are also to be seen everywhere on Seminole pastures. These humped gray creatures with wide, curved horns were originally imported from India and have now interbred with American cattle. They are widely distributed throughout Florida, since they do not mind the heat, flies, or mosquitoes. They have good resistance to the cattle diseases of this continent.

On the advice of trained government agents the

Seminole on the reservations have organized into stock associations for raising and selling their cattle. A man may borrow cattle to start a herd and repay the loan a few years later, adding one head for every ten borrowed.

Nowadays many Seminole are cowboys and range riders. They look very much like our Western cowboys, for they dress in the same jeans, felt hats, and high boots. You can see them in Florida rodeos and in the large towns where they deliver cattle. They swagger about, stiff-legged in their tight jeans and high boots.

More than half of the Seminole of Florida now live away from the reservations, in villages to the northeast of Lake Okeechobee or along the Tamiami Trail. Motorists are warned against speeding past these settlements by large signs along the road: *Slow—Indian Village*.

A Seminole village is usually encircled by a tall fence of poles. Over the entrance is a large sign which bears the name of the village. Many have been named after Osceola. Inside the fence, many of the villagers live in open-sided chickees, built just as their ancestors made them years ago.

The tourist who slows down in the hope of getting a glimpse of the people within the enclosed settlement will be disappointed. The Seminole inside are busy and they do not stand around the gates to be looked at. Occasionally a Seminole can be seen returning to the village from work. Only his darker skin color shows him to be an Indian. He cannot be recognized by his dress, since he wears the same jeans and work shirts as the other farmers of Florida. Some of the older men, however, still wear the long, colorful shirts. Seminole women are more easily recognized, for they wear the same long dresses as of old, made of hundreds of small pieces of bright cotton. Many still roll their long front hair over a piece of cardboard, in such a way that they look as though they were wearing a hat with a wide brim. Most of them continue to go about barefooted, and all wear a

few strings of beads, though not as many as their mothers wore years ago.

These village Seminole earn their living working for nearby truck farmers, helping to harvest beans, tomatoes, potatoes, lettuce, carrots. Some of the men work as mechanics in nearby factories. Many drive trucks.

The women put up small stands along the road, outside the tall fence of their village. They sell baskets, dolls, skirts and capes, small dugouts, wooden spoons, bows and arrows, birds which the old men have carved.

SEMINOLE   HANDCRAFTS

CARVED EGRET

COCONUT FIBER DOLL

POTTERY

Most of the women and girls standing in their colorful skirts and capes behind the counters know English, but they speak their own language among themselves. They are gay people and they talk a great deal. In front of tourists, however, their faces are grave and they speak very little, even though they understand everything that is said. After you have paid a Seminole girl for your purchase and told her how well the article is made, do not expect her to say thank you. The Seminole do not always understand such praise and, what's more, they see no reason for it. Every woman does her best as a matter of course. Praise to her face embarrasses her. She therefore says nothing and seems to wait patiently for you to go. She may not even see the need to answer your good-by.

For their holidays, many Seminole return to the reservations or to their villages. The Green Corn Festival is still the most important holiday. This dance is a four-day ceremony, which takes place in late June or early July in the southern Seminole settlements and in October or November among the northern Seminole. Even today, few white people ever see this dance. Only occasionally is a trusted white friend invited.

The celebration usually starts in the evening of each of the four days, when the fires are lighted, and continues far into the night. Men and women, boys and girls, dance their old dances and feast on corn mush, or *sofkee*, as the Seminole call it. Then they dance some more. During this festival they also hold council meetings to discuss Seminole business. If the council feels that anyone has not been behaving in a proper way, the elders reprimand him. White men are forbidden to attend these councils.

The Seminole also like to get together to celebrate some of the white men's holidays, particularly Christmas. During this holiday the minister on the reservation or the schoolteacher is in charge.

Florida, of course, does not have a white Christmas. Usually Christmas Day is bright and warm. Everywhere among the Seminole settlements Christmas trees stand gaily next to the open chickees, their bulbs glittering in the warm sun. Everyone rises early, even though men, women,

and children have been up late on Christmas Eve
enjoying family reunions and gossip.

Before the holiday, the little sewing machine
on the floor of each chickee throughout the settlements and reservations has been going full
blast. The mother, or a little girl by her side,
cranks the handle of the machine hour after hour,
stitching yards and yards of bright-colored strips

of cotton cloth. The Seminole have an excellent eye for arranging colors. They combine red and blue with yellow, green, orange, deep red, rose, purple, and white. The colors are not thrown together at random. They follow a set pattern, and the Seminole women are extremely clever in designing artistic color combinations. Each strip has a different design; in some, the bright colors make a zigzag pattern. The mother sews and fits these strips into skirts for herself and her daughter and shirts for her husband and son. Now gay new clothes are ready for the holidays. By Christmas Eve the sewing machines are all covered and will remain idle till after the New Year. Everyone is dressed in his best clothes.

Many of the children will go to the schoolhouse to eat Christmas dinner with their teacher. The women start for the cooking huts early, to prepare a large pot of stew for their own Christmas dinner, for stew is still the favorite Seminole dish.

Some tourists who came to visit a Seminole school one Christmas morning saw the girls and boys lined up in front of it. The girls wore long, wide, flowing skirts, and bright capes, and one or two strings of beads. Their long hair was loose and worn shoulder length. The boys wore jeans, plaid shirts, and bright green, red, or pink neckerchiefs. Some of the boys wore cowboy hats. Some had already buckled on the shiny pistols and holsters they had received as Christmas gifts from their parents or other relatives. All the children were barefooted. The older girls held the younger children by the hand as they trooped up the steps of the schoolhouse and entered the large classroom. The walls and ceiling of the room had been decorated for Christmas with the children's crayon drawings, cutout designs, and red and green crepe paper. The Christmas tree, which they had decorated themselves, stood in one corner and the children surrounded it.

This classroom was like thousands of others all

over the United States, yet it seemed different—
not because the children were all brown or because
the girls wore long, gay Seminole dresses, but
because of the way the children behaved. There
was as yet no teacher to watch them, nor had they
been told to keep still. Yet they were quiet and
spoke to each other in low voices, in Seminole.
"That is the way these Indian children always
behave," their teacher said later.

He came into the room, stepped over to the
tree, and picked up the first package. "Alice
Osceola," he read. A little girl stepped forward.

"Merry Christmas!" said the teacher.

"Merry Christmas and thank you," the little
girl said, in perfect English. She did not immediately unwrap her present; she held it under her
cape and waited till the other children received
theirs.

"John Micco," the teacher called out. "Merry
Christmas!"

"Merry Christmas and thank you," the boy

said quietly. He did not unwrap his present either.

The other children observed the same good manners. As the teacher called out their names— Billy Cypress, Billy Jumper, Willie Micco, Charley Osceola, Mary Cypress, Billie David—each

one said, "Merry Christmas and thank you," as the gift was presented.

Now that they all had their presents they unwrapped them, folding the bright string and the colored Christmas paper to take home with them. The little girls, who had received coloring books and crayons, seated themselves at their desks and began coloring their books.

A few older boys and girls who read English well received books. They, too, sat down and began to leaf through them. A few of the boys and girls received games of checkers and immediately formed teams to play. The teacher invited the visitors to play with the children. The children had all played checkers before and knew the rules. Some of them were good players, but they did not want to embarrass the visitors by beating them. They hesitated in their moves and made them slowly, so the visitors would not think they were trying to win the game.

The smell of roast turkey and buttered sweet potatoes made the children's mouths water. They stuck to their games but kept glancing shyly toward the swinging door which led to the kitchen.

Every time the door swung open they could see a long table with a white tablecloth, red Christmas candles, and a large bowl of fruit in the center.

"It is not very often that these boys and girls eat such a good dinner," the teacher explained. "The Seminole do not go hungry nowadays, but they are still poor. They do not get any help from the Federal government. Each of these youngsters will have to work hard to earn his own living when he grows up. But none of them is afraid of hard work," he added with pride.

INDEX

INDEX

* Indicates illustrations.